Disney Year Book 2008

FERN L. MAMBERG	Editorial Director
DEBBIE A. LOFASO	Creative Director
TERESA KLUK	Production Manager

PRINTED IN THE UNITED STATES OF AMERICA

ISBN-13: 978-0-545-02811-0
ISBN-10: 0-545-02811-6
ISSN: 0273-1274

Illustration Credits and Acknowledgments

6: Bettmann/Corbis. 7: The Granger Collection. 8: The Granger Collection. 9: © Keith Bedford/Reuters/Landov. 10: © Wendy Dennis/Visuals Unlimited. 11: © D. MacDonald/OSF/Animals Animals. 12: © J & B Photographers/ Animals Animals; © Wendy Dennis/Visuals Unlimited. 13: © D. McDonald/OSF/Animals Animals. 28: © Richard Czina/Circus Smirkus; © Circus Smirkus. 29: © Darren McCollester/Getty Images; © Circus Smirkus. 30: © Mim Leveque/Circus Smirkus. 31: The Granger Collection. 32: © Circus Smirkus; © Melanie Stetson Freeman/*The Christian Science Monitor* via Getty Images. 33: © Circus Smirkus. 48: © Stephen Dalton/Minden Pictures. 49: © Michael Durham/Minden Pictures; © Jeffrey Lepore/Photo Researchers, Inc. 50: © Miriam Silverstein/ Animals Animals. 51: © McDonald Wildlife Photography/Animals Animals; © K. Gowlett-Holmes/OSF/Animals Animals. 52: © Paul & Joyce Berquist/Animals Animals; © Leonard Rue Enterprises/Animals Animals. 53: © Stephen Dalton/Animals Animals. 54: © Traudel Sachs/Phototake, Inc. 55: © Sinclair Stammers/Photo Researchers, Inc.; © Mark A. Schneider/Visuals Unlimited; © E.R. Degginger/Animals Animals—Earth Scenes. 57: © Mark A. Schneider/Photo Researchers, Inc.; © William Weber/Visuals Unlimited; © Ken Lucas/Visuals Unlimited. 70-71: © John Shaw. 71: © Ken Davis/Tom Stack & Associates; © John Shaw; © Sylvain Cordier/ Peter Arnold, Inc. 72: © David Muench/Muench Photography Inc.; © John Shaw. 73: © John Shaw; © David Muench/Muench Photography Inc. 74: © Werner Layer/Animals Animals. 75: © Breck P. Kent/Animals Animals; © Tom & Pat Leeson/Photo Researchers, Inc.; © Arthur Morris/Visuals Unlimited. 76-77: Jackie Geyer—*Ranger Rick*. 92: © Owaki-Kulla/Corbis. 93: © PoodlesRock/Corbis. 94: © Photo by Stock Montage/Getty Images; The Granger Collection. 95: The Granger Collection; © Charlie Riedel/AP Photo.

Disney

Year Book 2008

SCHOLASTIC INC.

New York • Toronto • London • Auckland • Sydney • Mexico City • New Delhi • Hong Kong • Buenos Aires

Contents

A Closer LOOK
NATURE NOTEBOOK
PICTURE THIS!
TRY THAT!
BLAST FROM THE PAST

Robert Fulton's steamboat made its first trip up the Hudson River in 1807. Soon everyone wanted to travel by steam power!

Full Steam Ahead!

In 1807, Robert Fulton launched a steamboat in the Hudson River at New York City. People laughed. They called it "Fulton's Folly." A boat powered by a steam engine? It would never run, they said.

But Fulton proved them wrong. His steamboat traveled upriver from New York to Albany. The boat was a success! In 2007, people celebrated the 200th anniversary of that famous trip. Fulton's steamboat started a new age in travel.

Did You Know?
Fulton's boat was named the *Claremont*.

In Fulton's day, ships depended on the wind for long trips. They had tall masts and big sails to catch the breeze. Sailing ships traveled around the world. But if the wind didn't blow, the ships couldn't go. Travel was left to chance.

With steam power, people didn't need to wait for the wind. They could travel or ship goods anytime. Fulton didn't invent the steamboat. But he was the first to make steamboats practical. His was the first steamboat that could be counted on to make long trips.

A Great Inventor

Robert Fulton was born in Lancaster, Pennsylvania, in 1765. Even as a young boy, he loved inventions. While he was still in school, he designed a rocket and a hand-powered paddle-wheel boat.

Fulton was also a talented artist. As a young man he went abroad to study painting. But his real talent was figuring out how things worked—and how to make them work better. In England, Fulton invented a machine to dig canals. In France, he built a "diving boat"—a submarine. He even built a torpedo for the sub to carry!

By 1806, Fulton was back in the United States. He was ready to begin work on his steamboat.

A steam engine powered the *Claremont*. It turned two big paddle wheels, one on each side. They pushed the boat through the water.

Fulton began building his first steamboat in New York in 1806. It looked a lot like one of the sailing ships of that time. It had two masts and could put up sails if needed. But in the middle of the boat was a huge funnel. It belched black smoke from the boat's engine.

On August 17, 1807, Fulton and a few passengers boarded the boat for its trip to Albany. Many other people watched from the shore. The boat lurched forward. Then it suddenly stopped. Fulton quickly fixed the engine. The boat started out again. This time it kept going.

I love boat rides!

The boat had to go against the current to get to Albany. It traveled only 5 miles an hour, and the trip took 32 hours. But it showed that steamboats could travel rivers no matter what the current or wind. Fulton's boat was soon chugging up and down the Hudson River on regular runs, carrying paying passengers and cargo.

Fulton built several more steamboats before his death in 1815. And the popularity of these boats grew. Before long, steamboats were operating on many rivers. They helped America grow. They linked towns far from the sea with ports on the coast. And by 1838, steamboats were crossing oceans!

Freedom of the Seas

Ships have certainly changed since Robert Fulton's day. Just take a look at *Freedom of the Seas*. This cruise ship was launched in 2006. It is the largest passenger ship in the world. Fulton's boat was 142 feet long and 14 feet wide. *Freedom* is 1,112 feet long and more than 126 feet wide. It has 15 decks. And it can carry 4,000 passengers!

And passengers always have something to do. The ship has three swimming areas, including a wave pool. It has a miniature golf course, a basketball court, a climbing wall, even a skating rink. There are shops and restaurants. At night, 750,000 lightbulbs keep the ship bright. Robert Fulton would be amazed!

Meerkats always work together. You could say these little animals really stand up for each other!

THE MARVELOUS MEERKAT

If meerkats had a motto, it would be "Go team!" A meerkat's life is all about teamwork. These little animals live in groups. They do everything with their buddies. They hunt for food together. They guard each other. They even work together to raise their young.

Meerkats live in desert areas of southern Africa. Life is hard in their hot, dry land. But together, they survive.

Meerkats spend the day hunting for food. They eat insects, lizards, eggs, and plant bulbs. They even eat small snakes and birds. The meerkats scurry along on all fours. They sniff and scratch the ground. When a meerkat sniffs a tidbit, it digs for its dinner.

Standing guard: A meerkat can stand upright for long periods of time. The animal stiffens its tail and uses it for support.

Meerkats take turns standing guard as the group searches for food. When a guard senses danger, it peeps or barks a warning. This tells the other meerkats to run for cover!

Timon—A Meerkat Movie Star

Who is the world's most famous meerkat? Timon, of course! Timon is the brainy, happy-go-lucky meerkat in the Walt Disney film *The Lion King*. His motto is *hakuna matata*—"no worries." He is a nonstop chatterbox. And he loves to eat bugs. Timon isn't like other meerkats in some ways. He has left the hot, dry desert for a home in the jungle. His best buddy is Pumbaa, a warthog. And with Pumbaa, he befriends the young lion Simba. But like most meerkats, Timon is a loyal pal. He's ready to stand by his friends to the end.

Meerkat pups have nannies! When mom is out looking for food, another adult stays with the pups. Other adults also help groom and cuddle the young.

At night, the pack returns to its burrow. Meerkats are great diggers. They use their long claws to dig their burrows. Once inside, the meerkats pile on top of each other and go to sleep.

Baby meerkats, or pups, are born in litters of two to five. Their ears and eyes are closed for the first 10 to 14 days of life. They stay in the burrow. The mother nurses them. After a few weeks, she begins to bring them solid food.

Scorpions are a tasty treat for meerkats. But scorpions have poisonous stings. So adult meerkats must show pups what to do. First, adults give the pups dead scorpions. Later the pups get live scorpions with no stings. When they are ready, they get scorpions with stings.

"Say a few words for your fans," a scientist seems to ask. Meerkats grunt, bark, peep, trill, hiss, and growl.

As they get older, the pups go out with the pack to find food. Each youngster tags along with an older meerkat. That way, the adult can teach the pup the rules of hunting.

Even when they are full-grown, meerkats are small. An adult meerkat is about the size of a large squirrel. But these little animals can defend themselves. If they can't run from danger, they will stand and fight as a group. They fluff out their fur and stick their tails up in the air. They growl and hiss. Then they advance on their enemy, jumping into the air with each stride.

Meerkats are clever, comical, and full of spunk. These little animals make everyone smile!

DID YOU KNOW?

The name "meerkat" means "marsh cat" in Afrikaans, a language spoken in South Africa. But meerkats don't live in marshes. And they aren't cats. They are members of the mongoose family.

One morning, Lightning McQueen, Mater, and Sally were taking a quick oil break at Flo's Cafe. Suddenly a bright orange car zoomed past with a thunderous roar. It rattled windows and shook the ground.

"Whoa! Who's that?" McQueen asked.

"It's Snot Rod," Flo answered. "He just drove in last night, and he's been drag racing up and down Main Street ever since."

"Yup!" Mater added. "He's so fast and loud, everyone in Radiator Springs is ready to bust a hose."

"Well, he needs a little wheel-to-wheel talk about manners," McQueen said.

Just then, Snot Rod raced past again. Calmly, McQueen drove into the middle of the street. With a screech of tires, Snot Rod skidded to a stop.

"Outta my way!" he beeped. "I'm racin' here."

"No you're not," McQueen replied. "The racetrack and race-training camp are outside town. No one drag races down Main Street. It's rude—and dangerous."

Snot Rod revved his engine. "I'd like to see anyone in this one-horse-powered town stop me. Nobody's faster! I'm the street master! Why, I'm even faster than Lightning McQueen. He's nothin' but a fancy go-kart."

"Is that so?" McQueen replied. "Well, I happen to be Lightning McQueen. And I challenge you to a race. If I win, you either start acting right—or leave town. And if I lose, *I'll* leave."

His friends gasped. "McQueen! You can't do that!" Sally cried.

But McQueen wasn't worried. "I get to set the racing rules," he told Snot Rod. "Any four-wheeled fool can go fast for a couple of blocks. We'll do a distance race—one hundred miles. Then we'll see how fast you really are."

"Distance racing?" Snot Rod's engine whined. "I'm a street rod. I've never done that before! It's not fair."

"Neither is turning our town into your own race-track," McQueen answered. "Are you scared to try?"

"Scared? Not me!" Snot Rod replied. "Nobody's faster! I'm the street master!"

Everyone in Radiator Springs gathered to watch McQueen and Snot Rod start their race. As Sheriff dropped the green flag, Snot Rod and McQueen roared away. Soon the orange car was just a puff of dust in the distance. McQueen kept a steady speed. *Snot Rod drives fast,* he thought, *but he won't last. One hundred miles is a long race. I'll save my speed for when it counts.*

Then he saw something that made his oil boil. Snot Rod was leaving the road to take a shortcut. "Uh-oh," McQueen muttered. "That's cheating! But I'll show him—cheaters never win!"

McQueen put the pedal to the metal. He drove so fast the road blurred beneath his wheels. He could drive fair and still beat Snot Rod back to Radiator Springs. But as McQueen zoomed past the place where Snot Rod had left the road, he saw an old, battered sign: "Oil Leak Mines."

McQueen screeched to a halt. He knew old mines were dangerous places for cars. Hidden tunnels could give way under their wheels. There were hundreds of mine shafts hidden in the brush and rocks. A car could drive into one by accident and never get out again.

Even if it cost McQueen the race, he couldn't let Snot Rod drive into danger. With a chassis-shaking sigh, McQueen drove off the road and followed Snot Rod's tire tracks across the rocky ground. Suddenly he heard a loud crash, followed by loud horn blasts.

"Snot Rod's in trouble!" McQueen exclaimed. He headed in the direction of the wailing horn, driving carefully so he wouldn't end up in trouble, too.

At last McQueen came upon an old mine shaft. Boulders and fallen beams were scattered across the entrance. Rod's taillights blinked in the darkness below.

"Snot Rod! Are you okay?" McQueen shouted.

"McQueen? Help! I'm trapped!" Snot Rod yelled. He revved his engine, and more rocks tumbled down.

"Don't make any noise and don't move," McQueen commanded. "I'll go back to Radiator Springs for help!"

McQueen raced for town, driving faster than he'd ever gone before. "Hooray! McQueen won! McQueen won!" His friends poured into the street, honking their horns and blinking their lights.

McQueen stopped them. "No one has won," he said. "Snot Rod drove into a mine shaft at Oil Leak Mines. He needs help!"

The folks at Radiator Springs gasped. Snot Rod had been a loud, rude showoff. But no one wanted him to be in danger. They all hurried to the mines to help, pitching in to push boulders and beams out of the entrance. Then Mater lowered his cable, hooked Snot Rod's bumper, and cranked him up to safety. Snot Rod was embarrassed by his reckless behavior. But he was safe!

Snot Rod was towed back to town and quickly repaired. He looked as good as new.

"Thank you," Snot Rod said. "I guess I didn't really deserve all your help after the trouble I caused in town."

"We just did what we always do," Doc replied. "We take care of each other."

Snot Rod nodded. "I understand," he said. "McQueen took care of me—even though I didn't play fair. So that means he won. I'll leave."

But McQueen stopped him. "You don't have to go," he said. "You didn't win the race, but neither did I. We can both stay."

Snot Rod grinned, but then his smile faded. "What can I do in Radiator Springs?" he asked. "I only know how to drive fast."

"If I could deliver hot oil drinks to customers who don't have time to come to my cafe, it would be great for business," Flo said. "You could do that! But no drag racing, no speeding—and no short cuts!"

"That's a promise!" Snot Rod said. "Instead of street master, just call me the sip master!"

Everyone laughed, and Snot Rod knew that while he might have lost the race, he had won a town full of new friends.

TRY THIS!

COOL CAR CREATIONS

Lightning McQueen is a very cool race car. He loves cars—all kinds of cars—almost as much as he loves to race. You can make a race car like McQueen. Maybe he'll want to race you!

What You Need

white drawing paper, pencils, colored markers, poster paints, paintbrushes, safety scissors, aluminum foil, white glue

What You Do

1\. Draw a picture of a car on the white paper. You can use pictures in magazines for ideas. Or use your imagination to draw a fantasy car.

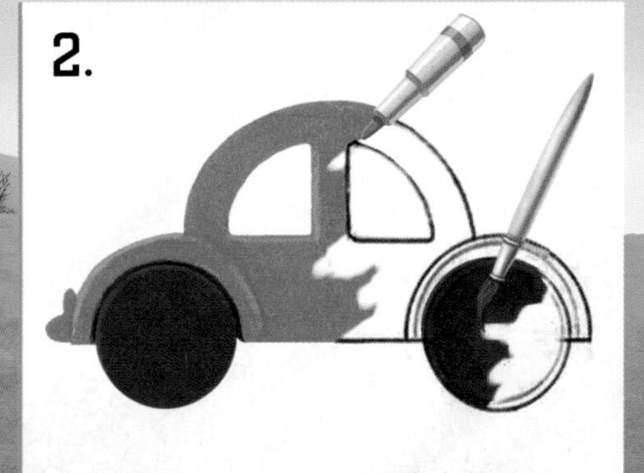

2\. Color the car with the markers or poster paints.

Work with an adult on this craft.

3.

Cut the aluminum foil to make hubcaps, bumpers, and an antenna. Glue them onto your car.

4.

Draw doors and door handles. You might want to lightly tint the windows.

5.

Use the poster paints to make your car stand out: stripes, circles, flames, flowers. Wow, what a car!

Now, why don't you make another fantasy car to race the first one? McQueen would be proud!

Kids of all ages are the stars at Circus Smirkus!

Circus Smirkus

Every summer some lucky young people head for a special circus. They share the fun of Circus Smirkus! Circus Smirkus is all about kids. Kids learn circus skills at Smirkus Camp, in Vermont. And kids with terrific skills can become Smirkus Troupers and star in a real circus show.

The Smirkus Camp runs sessions for different ages and levels. Smirkling Camp is a two-day camp for children 6 to 8 years old. They get to try basic circus skills like spinning plates, tumbling, and clowning.

There are one-week and two-week sleepaway sessions for young people ages 8 to 15. Campers learn acrobatics, juggling, and balance skills. They are introduced to aerial equipment such as the trapeze. And they learn clowning, dancing, and mime.

Advanced camp is for teens ages 14 to 18. They must have good circus skills. And they must try out for this camp. There are only 45 places.

The camp sessions end with an exciting show for family and friends. The campers get to show off all the circus skills that they have learned.

Skilled Smirkus Performers

At left, the kids perform an aerial act high above the ring. At right, a youngster twirls 21 hula hoops!

Kids with excellent skills can become Smirkus Troupers. The Troupers perform in a Big Top Tour—an actual circus show. For two months, they live the circus life. They may put on more than 70 shows in 15 towns, in a 750-seat Big Top tent!

The Troupers are 10 to 18 years old. The younger Troupers are the stars of the show. Older Troupers help out. And circus pros perform alongside them. The Troupers do everything you would expect to see in a circus. They are acrobats and jugglers. They perform on the trapeze and other aerial equipment. And, of course, they are Circus Smirkus clowns.

Kids love clowns. And kids can be clowns at Circus Smirkus!

History of the Circus

Circus shows have entertained people for more than 200 years. These shows began in England. At first, they showcased horseback riding. Then clowns were added. Soon there were acts of all kinds!

The circus came to the United States in 1785. The first American circus was put on in Philadelphia, Pennsylvania. George Washington, the nation's first president, was a circus fan. He even gave his white horse to the circus!

Soon circus shows were touring the country. They traveled by wagon and, later, train. At each town, the circus put up its tent and put on its show. In 1871, P.T. Barnum started a traveling circus he called "The Greatest Show on Earth." Barnum's circus later joined with other shows. It became the famous Ringling Bros. and Barnum & Bailey Circus.

Performing acrobatics on aerial silks (left) is a graceful circus art. Getting it right takes many hours of practice (below).

All the kids in the Big Top Tour have chores outside the ring as well. They help raise the tent and set up bleachers. They look after props and costumes. They even wash dishes. Circus life isn't all fun!

Each year's show has a different theme. Pirates, the Wild West, and superheroes have been themes in the past. Many shows are built around well-known stories. Favorites have included *Pinocchio* and *The Adventures of Robin Hood*. All the acts relate to the theme and help tell the story. There are colorful costumes and live music, too.

Kids who want to be in the show have to work hard on their skills. Then they have to try out. Even kids who have been Troupers before have to try out each year. They need to show that they have been improving and learning new skills. Only the best performers get to be part of the Big Top Tour.

Many young people at Circus Smirkus fall in love with the circus. A few may even think about becoming circus pros. But for most kids, their time at Circus Smirkus is a memory of great fun!

Circus Smirkus—by the Numbers

- ★ Number of Big Top Tour performances in 2007: 72
- ★ Number of Smirkus Troupers performing in the show: 25 (plus about 50 coaches, crew, and staff)
- ★ Size of the Big Top tent: 80 feet across
- ★ Number of trucks and trailers in the tour caravan: 23
- ★ Time it takes to set up the show: 8 hours
- ★ Number of red clown noses sold each year on tour: Over 1,500

DISNEY DELIVERY

Stamp collecting is a fun hobby. And here's an idea that is sure to get Mickey's "stamp" of approval—collect Disney postage stamps!

The United States has issued many Disney stamps over the years. But you don't have to stop at the U.S. border. Many other countries have issued stamps with Disney themes. There are hundreds and hundreds of different Disney stamps.

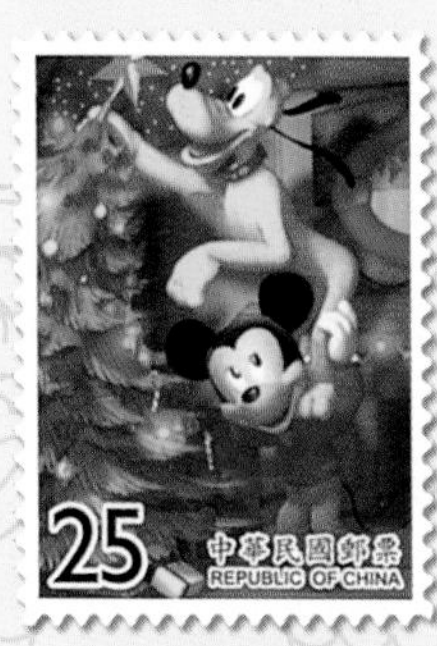

Collecting these stamps is like taking a trip around the world with your favorite Disney characters. Let Minnie Mouse show you the tiny country of San Marino in Europe. Fly with Peter Pan to the island of Dominica in the Caribbean Sea. Join Woody in the African country of Uganda.

The stamps shown on these pages are just a few of the many choices. In fact, there are so many Disney stamps that some people collect only one or two characters, such as Mickey Mouse or Donald Duck!

The Art of DISNEY

Abracadabra! Disney characters spread some magic on U.S. stamps in 2007. Four new stamps in a series called "The Art of Disney" were issued. The stamps were all on the theme of **magic**. One showed Mickey Mouse as the Sorcerer's Apprentice.

In 2006 the theme of the series was **romance**. Lady and Tramp were perfect for that group of four. In 2005 the theme was **celebration**. One of the four stamps showed Snow White and Dopey in a merry dance. And in 2004, when "The Art of Disney" series first began, the four stamps were on the theme of **friendship**. They showed a host of Disney friends, including Mufasa and Simba.

Would you like to collect all twelve of these special stamps?

HOME SWEET HOME

Winnie the Pooh sang to himself as he hurried home for lunch.

"Tum, tum, tumbly,
You're so grumbly,
Soon I'll fill you—
Up with honey."

It wasn't really time for lunch, but Pooh didn't like to argue with his tummy. After all, he had walked all the way to the Bee Tree and back. There weren't many bees in the tree, but Pooh was pretty sure they were somewhere making more honey. Why, he could almost hear them buzzing now.

Pooh opened the door to his home. The buzzing got louder. The bees had moved into his home! They had taken over his honeypots, and his honey shelf, and even the little scrap of honey toast he had left over from breakfast!

"Oh, bees," Pooh called out helpfully. "I believe you need to go home now. Your hive is quite empty."

The bees kept buzzing. They seemed to like Pooh's honey as much as he did.

"Oh, bother," said Pooh. "Now I shall have to think of something to do."

Pooh went to his Thoughtful Spot for a good Think. After many not-so-good Thinks, he finally thought of something good. "If the bees are living in my house," Pooh said, "then I shall move into theirs."

Pooh hurried back to the Bee Tree, trying not to mind the grumbling in his tummy. He stood at the bottom of the tree and looked up, up, up at the hive.

"Oh, dear," said Pooh. "I don't know that I can climb so high." He stared up at the little hive. "And I don't know that I will fit so well."

Pooh thought for a moment more. And perhaps, because it was feeling so grumbly, his tummy helped him out. "Owl's home is a much easier climb," said Pooh. "And it is much bigger. And Owl has honey."

Owl was very busy writing to his Great-Uncle Norbert when Pooh knocked. He listened to Pooh's story and nodded. "Why, yes, Pooh, I believe I could make room for you."

Pooh's tummy grumbled.

"And perhaps I could have just a bit of honey as a welcome?" Pooh asked hopefully.

"You may finish this." Owl handed Pooh a honeypot that had just a bit of honey. "I'm afraid I'm almost out."

Pooh's tummy felt much happier after that. But Pooh did wish for just a bit more honey. And really, Owl's house wasn't quite so large as Pooh had thought.

"Thank you for letting me stay here," Pooh said to Owl, "but I believe I might move to Rabbit's house now."

Rabbit had other ideas. "Oh, no, no, no, Pooh Bear! Do you remember the last time you came into my house? You ended up stuck in the door! Why, I had to make a mantelpiece out of the back of you! What's wrong with your house, anyway?"

"The bees have moved in," Pooh said. "So I had to move out. I suppose I could ask Piglet. I could probably make the trip to his house sooner if my tummy wasn't so very empty. I've just had the littlest bit of honey at Owl's."

Rabbit frowned, but he gave Pooh a small dish of honey.

Pooh finished Rabbit's honey, cleaning the dish out very nicely. Then he went on to Piglet's house and told him about the bees.

"Oh, dear, Pooh," said Piglet. "That's terrible. Of course you can move into my house." But Piglet's house was built for a Very Small Animal, not for a Bear Stuffed with Fluff. And Piglet had just used up all his honey to make sweet haycorn muffins. Pooh's tummy began to grumble again.

"Thank you, Piglet," said Pooh, "but perhaps I should try Eeyore's house."

Eeyore had just finished rebuilding his house of sticks when Pooh arrived. "Be glad to share," Eeyore said, "but the house is a little—"

Pooh didn't wait to hear the rest. He pushed his way into Eeyore's house, knocking it down.

"—fragile," Eeyore finished.

"Oh, dear. I'm sorry, Eeyore. Perhaps I could help you rebuild." Pooh stood up and stepped on some of the sticks, snapping them in two.

"Thanks, Pooh," Eeyore said. "I'll let you know if I need your help."

Pooh wasn't sure what to do now. Before he could think much more, though, Tigger bounced over and knocked him onto the two sticks that Eeyore had just stood up together.

"How nice," said Eeyore. "Now I don't have to worry about when it will fall again."

"What's the matter, Buddy Bear?" Tigger asked. "You look as down as old Long Ears here."

"The bees have moved into my home," said Pooh. "I don't suppose I could move into yours?"

"Woo-hoo-hoo!" shouted Tigger. "We'll be roommates! Best bouncin' buddies forever! We'll have the best bouncin' house in the Hundred-Acre Wood! Let me go tell Roo and Mrs. Kanga, too! We'll have a Welcome New Roommate Bouncin' Party!"

Pooh grew tired just watching Tigger bounce off. He walked slowly to his Thoughtful Spot. Tigger's house would be a very bouncy place to live. That left only Kanga's house. And she and Roo were already two.

"Perhaps," Pooh thought, "I should look through the Wood again. Maybe I can find another home that will be big enough and strong enough and filled with enough honey."

Tired and a little grumbly, Pooh set off through the Wood one last time. After a while he came to a lovely Pooh-sized house in a tree. It had a bell with a sign.

Pooh rang the bell and stepped inside. This house had a Pooh-sized door and Pooh-sized table and chairs! This house was sturdy. And best of all, this house had shelves of shiny honeypots.

"Why, this home is just like my old one!" Pooh said.

"It *is* your old one, Pooh Bear!" Rabbit stepped inside, holding a mop. "We just cleaned up the honey mess. But you'll have to do that yourself next time."

"Yes, dear," explained Kanga, "if you keep the honeypots clean, the bees won't take over your house."

"But you can still come over for a bounce anytime, Buddy Bear," said Tigger.

"And I've made a special sign so that you will always remember this is your home," said Owl.

Pooh took the sign and admired the honeypot on it. "Yes," he said. "Surely home is where the honey is!"

An African chameleon flicks out its long, sticky tongue to catch the insects that it eats.

Secret Weapons

It's rude to stick out your tongue. But it isn't rude if you are a lizard! Some lizards use their tongues to catch their meals. One of these lizards is the African chameleon. Its tongue is almost as long as its body! When the chameleon sees a tasty insect, it shoots out its tongue. The tongue has a sticky tip. It snags the insect and pulls it back into its mouth.

This special tongue is the chameleon's secret weapon! Many other animals have secret weapons, too.

Feeding and fighting: The leopard at left is a hunter. Its sharp fangs help it catch prey. The grizzly bear below can use its heavy claws to fight off enemies.

These wildlife weapons help animals get food. They also help animals fight off enemies. And each kind of animal has its own way of doing these things.

Many hunting animals have sharp teeth. In the wild, they use these weapons to catch their food. The mouth of a lion or leopard, for example, has four extra-long, pointed teeth. These are called fangs.

Don't Step on Me!

The little stonefish lives in shallow waters off the coast of Australia. It doesn't look dangerous. It hides among the stones and litter at the bottom. Its body is covered with warts and slime. It looks just like a stone. But you don't want to step on it! A stonefish has 13 sharp spines on its body. The spines contain a powerful poison. The stonefish is the world's deadliest poisonous fish.

Many kinds of fish use poison as a weapon. Other animals use poison as well. Hornets, wasps, and bees do. So do spiders and some snakes. But few of these animals are as dangerous as the stonefish.

A wild cat's long, curved claws are as dangerous as its teeth. Cats use their claws to hook their prey and pull it down. Most cats can pull their claws back into their toes. A cat usually keeps its claws pulled in. When it fights, it pushes its claws out.

Not all animals with claws use them for hunting. Bears and raccoons, for example, use their claws mainly for digging and climbing. But when necessary, their heavy claws can be used to fight off enemies.

Some animals use teeth to bite. Some use claws to fight. And some animals use spines to stab.

A porcupine has thousands of sharp spines called quills. When a porcupine is frightened, its quills stand up from its body. The animal turns its quill-covered tail toward an enemy and whips it back and forth. If the enemy doesn't back off, the porcupine gives it a swat with its tail. The tail drives the needlelike quills into the enemy. Ouch!

Many kinds of fish also have sharp spines. The porcupine fish is one. Its spines lie flat until the fish is scared. Then the fish gulps water. Its body swells up like a balloon. Its spines stick out in all directions. A bigger fish will think twice before trying to swallow this prickly ball!

When a skunk lifts its tail, watch out! The skunk will twist its body around and fire its smelly spray at an enemy.

The skunk has a secret weapon, too. It sprays a stinky liquid from beneath its tail! The skunk's spray isn't harmful. But it smells so bad that other animals learn to leave skunks alone.

Some weapons grow out of an animal's head! Goats, sheep, cattle, and other grazing animals have horns that they use to defend themselves. These animals prefer to run from danger. But when they are cornered, they lower their heads. Then they batter their enemies with their horns and chase them away.

Dall sheep have thick, curled horns. They can use these remarkable weapons like battering rams.

Mother goats will use their horns to protect their babies, or kids, from danger. A mother goat has even been known to kill a bear with her horns to defend her kid! The horns of goats, sheep, and cattle keep growing throughout the animals' lives. Deer have antlers, which are a lot like horns. But their antlers last for only part of the year. The animals shed their antlers each winter. Then they grow new antlers in spring.

As you can see, every kind of animal has its own special weapon. These weapons may keep the animal safe. They may help the animal get food. Or they may do both jobs. Each animal uses the secret weapons it was born with. They help the animal stay alive for another day.

The Swimming Water Gun!

The archerfish may have the most amazing weapon of all. It shoots water bullets!

This little fish lives in Australia and parts of Asia. It hides just below the surface of a pond. There it waits for an insect to crawl onto a branch or leaf hanging over the water. Then the fish takes aim. Using its tongue, it forces a jet of water droplets from its mouth. The stream of water knocks the insect off its perch. It falls into the water. In a flash, the archerfish gobbles it up.

A Closer LOOK

This crystal is tourmaline. It is called the "gemstone of the rainbow" because it comes in so many different colors.

Crystal Clear

A crystal is like a pretty flower made of stone!

Emeralds, amethysts, topazes—these are beautiful gems. They glitter in the light. They glow with color. And they are special. These gems are all crystals. There are many other kinds of crystals, too. But only some crystals are lovely gemstones.

Agate is a gemstone that has curved bands of rich color. Long ago, people thought that wearing agate made people like you.

Rose Quartz is a lovely rosy-pink color. Some people used to believe that this crystal could get rid of anger.

Crystals form when liquids change to solids, as when water freezes into ice. The tiny particles that make up the liquid lock together to form the solid. They do this in set patterns, forming crystals.

Crystals are all around you. Most are too small to see without a microscope. Salt and sugar are made of crystals. So are snowflakes and sand. But the most beautiful crystals are gemstones, like the ones shown on these pages.

Topaz comes in many colors. Long ago, people thought that this gemstone brought good health and helped people sleep.

Making Crystal Candy

Rock candy is made up of big sugar crystals. It's easy to make. Ask an adult to help. You can watch the crystals form and have a yummy treat!

What You Need

- a saucepan
- 1 cup of water
- 2 cups of sugar
- clean cotton string
- a pencil
- 3 paper clips
- a wide-mouthed jar

What You Do

1. Boil the water. Slowly add the sugar. Stir until all the sugar dissolves. Let the mixture cool.
2. Cut three pieces of string. Tie them to the pencil, as shown here. Attach a paper clip to the bottom of each piece of string. 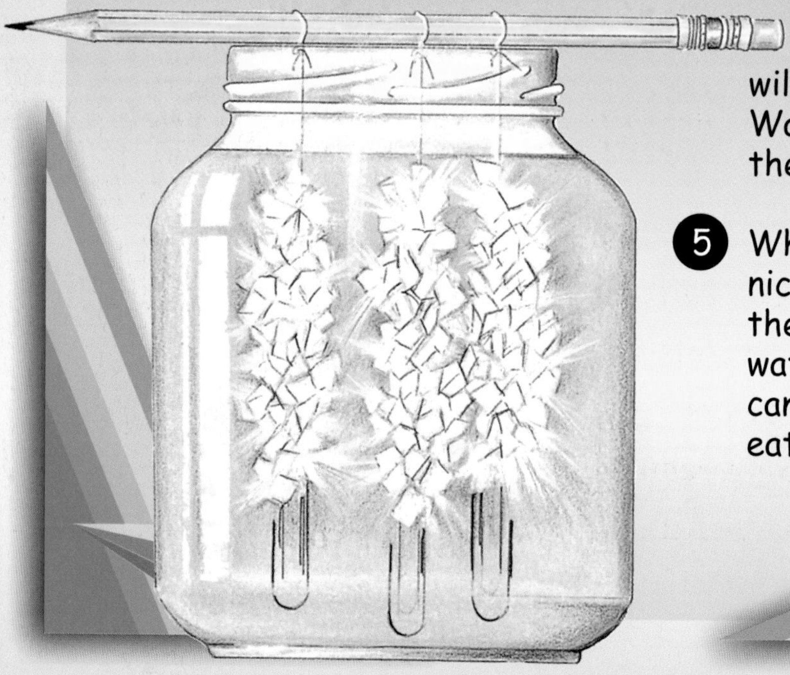
3. Pour the sugar-water mixture into the jar. Lay the pencil across the rim of the jar, so the strings hang down into the mixture.
4. In a few hours, sugar crystals will begin to form on the string. Over a period of several days, the crystals will get larger and larger. Watch, but don't jiggle the jar.
5. When the crystals are nice and big, remove the strings from the water. Your crystal candy is ready to eat!

Amethyst is purple in color. It was once believed that this gemstone could protect soldiers from harm.

Emerald is a rich green crystal. Some people believed that wearing an emerald could help fight sadness.

People have long used gems to make jewelry. And over the years, people have had many strange beliefs about crystals. Some thought crystals had special powers. Fortune tellers gazed into crystal balls to see the future. And some crystals were said to be magical—they could protect people from harm and illness.

Today, most people don't believe that crystals have mystical powers. They love crystals because they are beautiful.

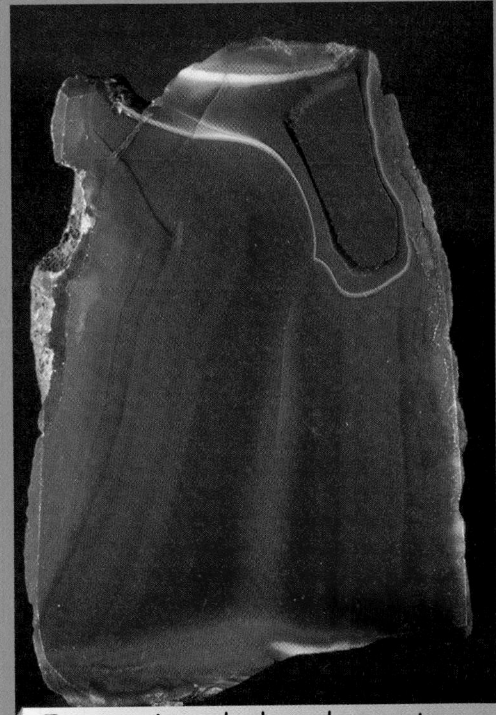

Jasper is a dark red gemstone. In ancient times, people believed that jasper could cure snakebites.

Tink and the Ever Spring Festival

"Queen Clarion has announced her Ever Spring Festival!" Tinker Bell called to her friends, waving a golden invitation. The Ever Spring Festival was one of the biggest celebrations in Pixie Hollow. All the fairies of Pixie Hollow took pride in using their talents to make it special.

"We just received our golden announcements, too!" Fira said. "We were all talking about what we were going to do to make it the best festival ever!"

"Yes," Rani chimed in. "I'm going to start working on something wonderful—just as soon as I think of it!" One by one, the fairies flew away, their happy laughter floating after them.

Tink went to her cozy teakettle workshop, where she did all her tinkering and mending. She picked up her tiny hammer and began to work on a pot that needed fixing. She always thought best when her hands were busy.

But although she tapped and tapped on the pot, no new ideas came to her.

Suddenly, Vidia stood in Tink's doorway. "Why, Tinker Bell," she said, with a nasty smile. "I can't believe you're hammering on that dented old pot when the Ever Spring Festival is coming! Shouldn't you be working on a fabulous idea?"

But Tinker Bell wasn't going to let Vidia bother her. "I'm thinking," she said. "Maybe you should go home and think, too. Even pots and pans ideas are better than no ideas at all!"

"Hmph!" Vidia huffed, and she flew away.

I need some inspiration, Tinker Bell thought. Perhaps talking to my friends will give me an idea.

Tink flew to see Bess, an art-talent fairy. Bess was painting with big splashes of beautiful color.

"I'm painting our portraits to show at the festival," Bess told Tinker Bell. "But I don't know how to hang them up."

"I'll help you," Tinker Bell said. But watching Bess paint didn't give Tink any new inspiration.

Tink decided to see what Rani was doing. Rani was a water-talent fairy, so Tinker Bell found her beside the stream. She was shaping water into perfect sparkling balls.

"Hello, Tinker Bell," she said. "I think I'll make a fountain that juggles balls of water. Could you help me build it?"

"Of course," Tink answered. "I'll come back later to help you. Right now, I have to look for my own inspiration."

Tink flitted to Lily's garden and touched down beside her.

"Tink! I'm so glad you're here!" Lily said. "I want to make flower garlands for the festival, but my flowers are thirsty, and my best watering can won't sprinkle!"

Tink carefully looked at Lily's watering can. Sure enough, pebbles were stuck in the spout, stopping the water from pouring out. Tink quickly pulled the pebbles out.

"Thank you!" Lily called as Tink flew away.

Soon Tink spotted Terence sitting at his desk. He was trying to think of a new game for the fairies to play at the Festival. Tink always has very good ideas, Terence thought. I'll ask her!

But Tinker Bell didn't have any ideas for Terence. "I'm looking for inspiration myself," she said. "That's why I'm visiting my friends. I'm going to see Dulcie next. You can come, too."

Dulcie, a baking-talent fairy, was making whipped-cream tarts.

"Tink, my best spoons and favorite ladle are bent," Dulcie said. "Can you fix them?"

Before Tink could reply, Prilla ran into the kitchen.

"I can hardly wait for the Ever Spring Festival!" Prilla declared, turning cartwheels around the table.

Suddenly, Prilla bumped into the table and knocked a pot of green peas to the floor. Peas bounced across the room—straight toward the whipped-cream tarts.

In a flash, Tink and Terence grabbed Dulcie's spoons and batted the peas back into the pot.

And just like that, Tink had her inspiration!

"Come on, Terence," she shouted. "I know what we can do for the Festival!" She explained her idea to Terence while she gathered pots, pans, jugs, spoons, and ladles. Then they hurried to ask Lily for lots of fresh green peas.

On the day of the Ever Spring Festival, all the fairies came dressed in their prettiest clothes. Everyone admired Bess's beautiful portraits, Rani's fountain, and Lily's garlands. And Dulcie's tarts were delicious.

Then Tinker Bell and Terence gave everyone spoons, ladles, and green peas and showed the fairies how to hit the peas into the pots, pans, and jugs placed around the green. Soon everyone was laughing and shouting as they played the new game Tink had invented—Pea Pot Croquet!

Everyone loved the game. Tink was very happy.

"I was worried I wouldn't do my part to make the Ever Spring Festival a success," she told her friends.

"But Tinker Bell, think of all you did for us," Rani pointed out. It was true. Tinker Bell had helped all her friends prepare for the Festival.

"Three cheers for Tinker Bell," they shouted. Tink smiled at them.

"Three cheers for friends!" Tink said. "The best inspiration of all!"

A brown bird called a bittern is hiding in the tall grass of this marsh. Can you find it?

Wetland Wonderlands

There is dry land. There is open water. And in between the two are wetlands. A wetland is a place where water and land seem mixed together. You may stand on land, but water is all around you. There are quiet pools and slow-moving streams. And the ground under your feet is wet and squishy.

Wetlands are special places. Wild animals of all kinds make their homes there. The air is filled with the songs of birds and insects. You may see strange plants that are found nowhere else. Let's visit some of these wet wonderlands!

Did You Know?

Marshes, bogs, and swamps are all wetlands.

In a marsh: A sticky sundew traps a damselfly (left). A raccoon hunts for food (above). And a snake moves among water lilies (below).

Marshes are watery places with lots of plants. Tall grasslike plants called sedges grow at the water's edge. Water lilies float on the water. And sometimes there are strange plants like the sundew. These plants trap and eat insects!

There are always lots of insects in a marsh. There are lots of birds, too. And if you wait quietly, you may see other animals as well.

Spongy moss covers the surface of a bog. Other plants grow there, too.

Bogs form where the ground dips low. Water collects in these places. Plants die and rot in the shallow water. Some float up to the surface. Spongy moss grows among the rotting plants. In time, a mat of moss covers the water surface. It may be thick enough to walk on. But it shakes and quakes beneath your feet!

Rare wildflowers grow in bogs. You can find insect-eating plants there, too. You will see different birds in the bushes. Some make their nests there. Others come to look for food.

In a bog: A frog rests in the shallow water (top left). Lady's slipper orchids bloom (left). Pitcher plants lie in wait for insects (above).

There aren't too many other animals in bogs. But you will often find frogs in these places. Frogs love bogs!

Frogs belong to a group of animals called amphibians. They spend the first part of their lives in water, as tadpoles. They look like little fish. But then they grow legs. They hop out of the water to live on land as frogs. A wetland, where water and land are mixed, is a perfect home for a frog!

Egrets wade amid tall grasses and hummocks in Florida's Everglades.

In **swamps**, trees grow alongside other plants. One of America's largest swamps is the Everglades, in southern Florida. Much of this huge wetland is covered by shallow water. Tall sawgrass grows from the water. When it waves in the breeze, it makes the swamp seem to be a river of grass.

Small islands called hummocks rise above the sawgrass. Trees, shrubs, and vines grow on the hummocks. Turtles and alligators crawl out of the water to sun themselves here. The hummocks are also good nesting places for birds. Birds are everywhere in the Everglades. The swamp is full of wading birds, such as egrets. There are ducks and geese, too.

In the Everglades: An alligator takes a sunbath (top). A Florida panther rests beneath a cypress tree (above). And a spoonbill is reflected in the water (right).

In other places there are groves of trees. Cypress, mangrove, and other trees grow in the Everglades. Moss grows on their trunks. The trees shade the damp ground. The water is dark. Here you may see larger animals, such as deer. You may even spot a rare Florida panther.

The Everglades covers over two million acres. Much of this area is a national park. It is truly a wet, wild wonderland!

PICTURE THIS!

WHAT AM I?

Here's an animal you will never see—even if you travel to every zoo in the world! This odd-looking creature has fur, feathers, scales, a tough hide, claws, and hooves, all at the same time. It has a big hump and two different pairs of wings.

Its four legs don't match. Its tail is huge. It has floppy ears, branching antlers, bug-out eyes, and a very strange nose.

Which real animals were used to create this mystery creature? Find each numbered part, and guess what animal it comes from.

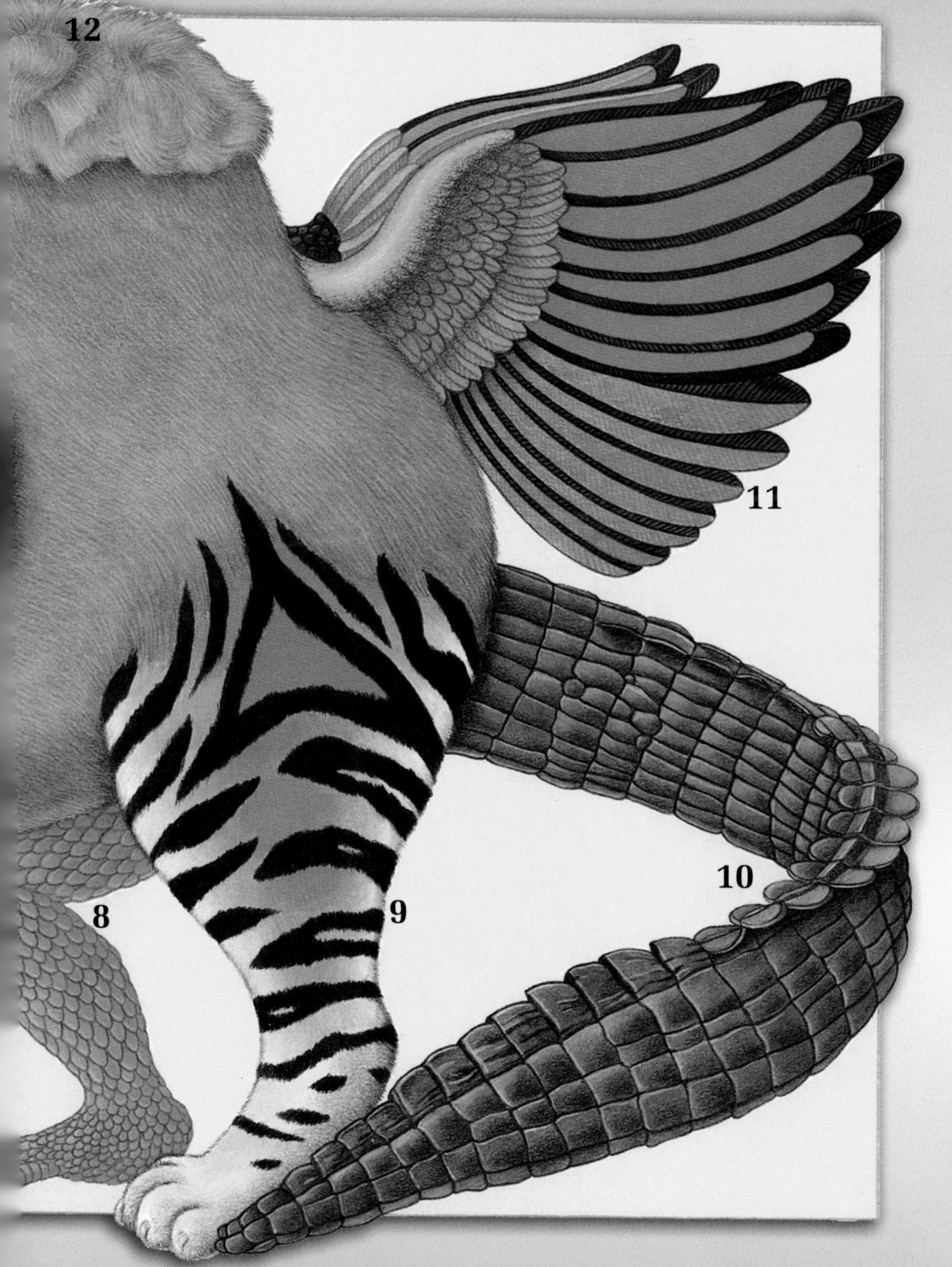

Answers

1. moose
2. frog
3. elephant
4. anteater
5. snake
6. sloth
7. zebra
8. lizard
9. tiger
10. alligator or crocodile
11. bird
12. camel
13. butterfly

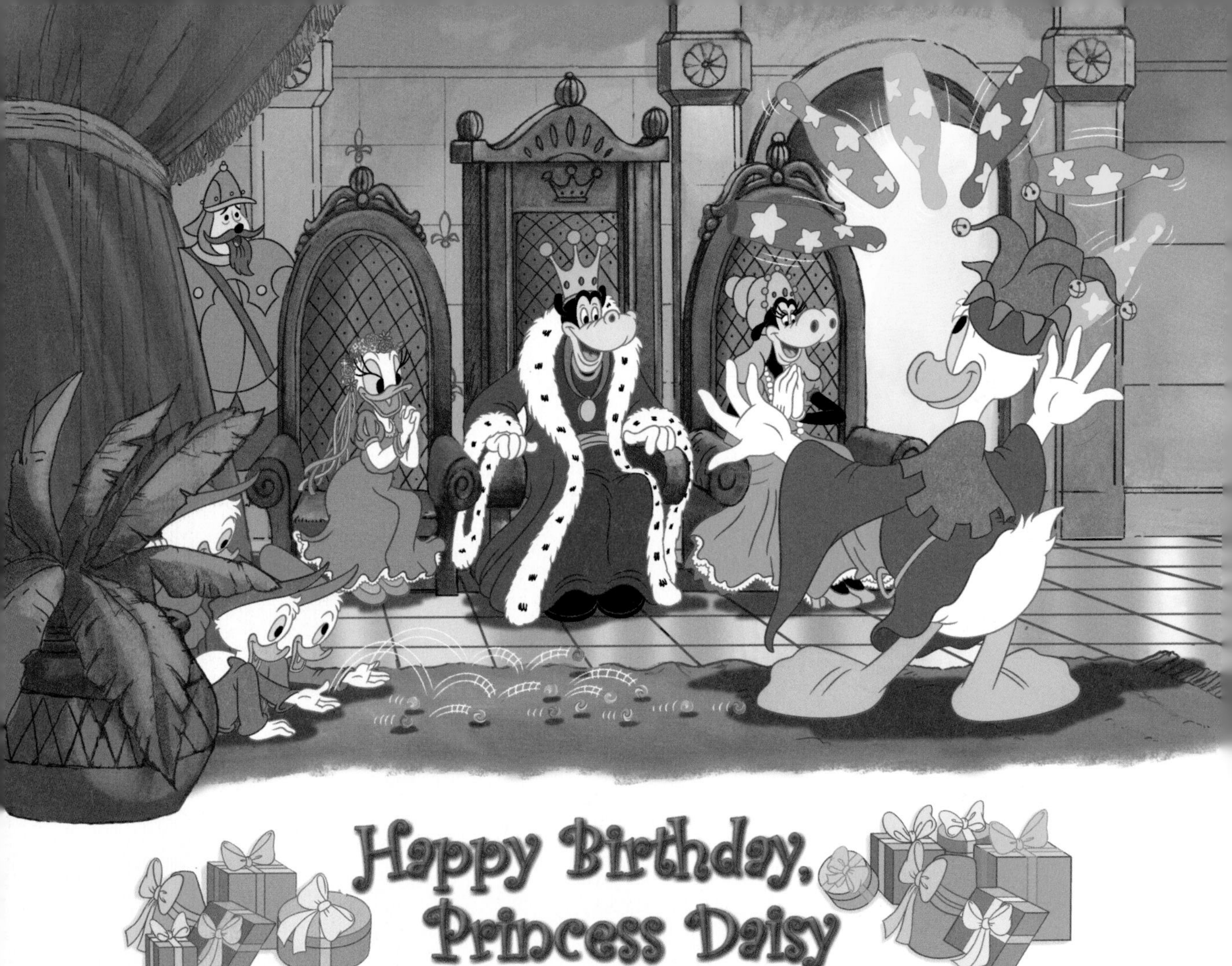

Happy Birthday, Princess Daisy

"For you, my princess," said jester Donald Duck, with a bow and a flourish. Donald presented Princess Daisy with one perfect flower, a rose. It was how he always began his act—a bow, a flourish, and a flower.

Princess Daisy, Queen Clarabelle, and King Horace watched as Donald then tossed one, two, three, four, five, six clubs in the air to juggle. "Tah-dah!" he said, catching and tossing each club with ease. Then Huey, Dewey, and Louie, the mischievous royal pages, rolled some of their royal marbles onto the floor!

All six clubs went flying. "Waak?!" cried Donald, dancing on the marbles and trying to keep his balance. The pages raced out. Each one caught two clubs just as Donald landed on his tail feathers.

The royal family laughed and applauded. They thought it was all part of the act. The king and queen thought their jester was terrifically amusing. Princess Daisy just thought the royal jester was terrific.

Donald bowed, picked up his clubs, and left the royal presence. "Another act ruined!" he muttered. "And in front of the princess, too!" He shook his head. Donald thought Princess Daisy was the most beautiful, most perfect princess ever.

After each performance, Donald went to the one place where he could do the one thing that no one else could mess up. He had a small gardening shed in a little-used corner of the castle grounds. No one knew about his special place. It was filled with pots and soil and plants. And it was where he grew the lovely flowers he gave to the princess.

But today, after the pages had messed up his act, Donald was really upset! "Those boys!" he grumbled as he was preparing some soil to put into a pot. "If they weren't my nephews, I'd—" He saw a strange pink seed and absentmindedly tossed it into a trash barrel. It missed the trash and landed in a flowerpot on a table behind him. Donald was too angry to even notice.

Later that afternoon, the royal trumpeter blew his trumpet in front of the castle. The townspeople gathered. The royal pages watched from a castle window. The neighborhood giant cocked an ear to hear. And the local dragon took to the air so it wouldn't miss hearing the royal news.

Donald hurried back to the castle and heard, "Hear ye, hear ye! One week from tonight, in honor of Princess Daisy's birthday, King Horace and Queen Clarabelle will give a ball. All loyal subjects and creatures in the kingdom are invited! All may bring Princess Daisy a birthday present! And whoever gives Princess Daisy the best present shall be presented with a chest of gold!"

Sir Goofy turned to Sir Mickey and asked, "Gawrsh, what does a princess need?" Sir Mickey said, "I don't know. What does a princess want?" Donald added, "What do you give a princess who has everything?"

The next day, Donald entertained the royal family and began by presenting the princess with a flower. But the troublesome trio were about to mess up his acts.

As Donald was telling the king his favorite joke ("So, Your Majesty, where does an eight-hundred-pound king sit?") the boys pulled the rug out from under him!

A flustered Donald muttered, "Now, where was I?" King Horace laughed and said, "You were telling my favorite joke. The answer is. . .'Anywhere he wants to!' "

Donald was getting more and more annoyed. He tried to go on to his next act. But when he performed his magic trick of fire, Huey, Dewey, and Louie opened a window, and the draft put out the flame. When he did his juggling act, they grabbed all his props and ran away with them.

Really, really angry, Donald chased the mischievous pages around and around the royal throne as they giggled and laughed. He had almost caught them when the royal tutor announced it was time for their lessons.

Donald was still sputtering when he remembered he was with the royal family.

Queen Clarabelle and Princess Daisy just smiled. The king just loved the jokes. Queen Clarabelle just loved the jester's acts. Princess Daisy just loved the jester!

After the performance, Donald went to his gardening shed. He didn't notice the new and fabulous flower growing in the corner flowerpot. He was too busy trying to think of a birthday present for the princess.

Finally, the big night arrived—and so did the whole kingdom! The royal trumpets blared as King Horace, Queen Clarabelle, and Princess Daisy greeted their guests. Again the trumpeters trumpeted, "Rah-tah-tah-tah!" All the subjects and all the creatures in the kingdom sang a happy birthday song to Princess Daisy.

"Thank you, everyone!" said the princess. "This is the best birthday party ever!"

And indeed it was! The butcher cooked Daisy's favorite meal. The baker baked a birthday cake big enough for the whole kingdom. The candlestick-maker made pink candles for the cake. The milliner made elegant party hats. The dragon roasted marshmallows for everyone. The neighborhood giant was outside giving piggyback rides to one and all.

The tables were filled with presents for the princess. Sir Mickey gave her a box of chocolates wrapped in a big pink bow. Sir Goofy gave the princess a picture he had drawn of her. Huey, Dewey, and Louie gave her a ball, a stick, and a baseball glove.

Donald *did* find something to give the princess. He stood shyly at the end of the very last table next to a flowerpot. Growing in the pot was a single flower, unlike any flower anyone had ever seen. Princess Daisy looked at it in amazement. Donald said, "Your Highness, the bright orange center is for your sunny smile. The petals are pink for your favorite color. And see how the tips curl, just like your beautiful eyelashes."

"Oh, Donald!" exclaimed Princess Daisy. "This is the most beautiful flower I have ever seen anywhere in the kingdom! What is it called?"

Donald looked around to see if Huey, Dewey, and Louie were going to mess him up again. Happily, the boys were nowhere in sight. Donald turned to the princess and proudly said, "I have named this new flower the Princess Daisy daisy."

Can you guess which birthday present Princess Daisy liked best?

A Crown for a Princess

Princess Daisy loves wearing her pretty flower crown. You can make a crown of flowers for yourself—and feel just like a princess!

What You Need

- 4 long green pipe cleaners
- flowers and leaves (fresh, silk, or plastic)
- small colored beads
- 5 or 6 different colors of ribbon
- white glue

What You Do

1. Securely twist one end of a pipe cleaner to the end of another one. Do the same with the other two pipe cleaners. Now wrap the two long pipe cleaners around each other to create one thick strand.

2. Place the thick pipe-cleaner strand around your head so that it fits perfectly. Twist the ends together. This is the base of your crown.

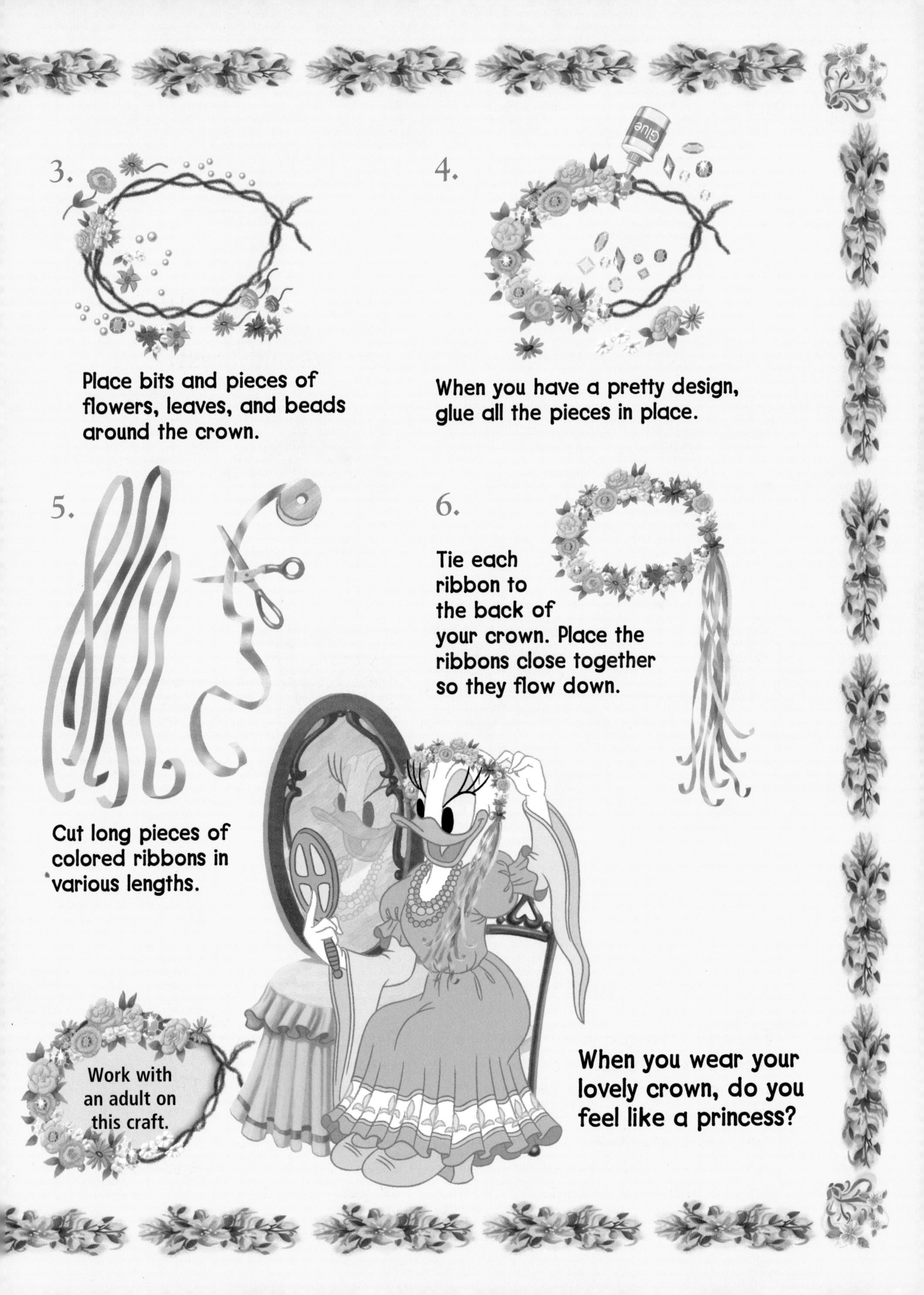

3.

Place bits and pieces of flowers, leaves, and beads around the crown.

4.

When you have a pretty design, glue all the pieces in place.

5.

Cut long pieces of colored ribbons in various lengths.

6.

Tie each ribbon to the back of your crown. Place the ribbons close together so they flow down.

Work with an adult on this craft.

When you wear your lovely crown, do you feel like a princess?

PRESIDENTIAL ROCK STARS

Four giant faces look out from the side of Mount Rushmore in South Dakota. They are portraits of four great American presidents. The faces are carved right into the stone of the mountain. These presidents are "rock stars"!

Wow! What great faces!

Every year, millions of people come to see Mount Rushmore. It is a famous national memorial. No wonder South Dakota's slogan is "Great Faces, Great Places."

There have been 43 U.S. presidents in all. But just four presidents are on Mount Rushmore. Each of the four has a special place in American history.

If you were to stand facing the mountain, here's what you would see. The first face on the left would be that of George Washington. He was the first U.S. president. Next to Washington is Thomas Jefferson. He was the third president and helped the country grow. Then comes Theodore Roosevelt, the 26th president. He led the way in saving America's forests and wild lands. And on the right is Abraham Lincoln, the 16th president. He led the country through the Civil War.

George Washington was the top American general in the Revolutionary War. Thanks to him, the United States won its independence from Great Britain. He became the first U.S. president in 1789. That's why Washington's portrait stands out most on Mount Rushmore.

A sculptor named Gutzon Borglum designed the Mount Rushmore memorial. He also directed the carving at the mountain. The work took 14 years from start to finish!

Thomas Jefferson wrote the Declaration of Independence in 1776. As president, he bought the huge Louisiana Territory from France. It doubled the size of the country. He was also a scientist and an inventor. And he loved to garden and play the violin.

The work began in 1927. About 400 people worked on the project at different times. Their jobs were very hard—and dangerous, too.

Workers started each day by climbing 700 steps to the top of the mountain. Then they were lowered onto the face of the mountain. It was a 500-foot drop. But steel cables held them safely. The workers used dynamite to blast tons of rock from the face of the mountain. The last few inches of the giant portraits were carved with hand tools.

Abraham Lincoln was president during the Civil War, in the 1860's. He kept the country from breaking apart. He was also the president who ended slavery in the United States. Lincoln stood 6 feet 4 inches tall. He was the tallest American president ever!

Theodore Roosevelt created many new national parks and forests. He was president at the start of the 20th century. That was a time of great change. There were many new inventions. Roosevelt was the first president to travel in a car, an airplane, and a submarine.

The presidential portraits on Mount Rushmore are really, really big. From the chin to the top, each head is as tall as a five-story building. The presidents' noses are as long as delivery trucks. And each of their mouths is almost as wide as a two-lane road!

Mount Rushmore's giant carvings are an amazing sight. And the mountain country around the memorial is beautiful, too. This wonderful place is an American national treasure.

The stone portraits were scrubbed clean in 2005. It was their first cleaning since they were carved into the mountain.

What did the cat say when it fell down?

Me-OW!

What kind of dinosaur is always ready for bed?

A Pajamasaurus Rex!

What did one elevator say to the other?

I think I'm coming down with something!

What did the mother snake say to her baby at bedtime?

Coil up and go to sleep!

What do you call a pooch that lives in Alaska?

A chilly-dog!

What flowers grow right under your nose?

Tulips!

What has four legs and goes oom-oom?

A cow walking backward!